This Notebook Belongs To:

....

FEATHER
PRESS

How to use this notebook

All you need is a pen to get started, every day you need to write at less 3 words to complete this language and moving to the next language, And keep writing to the last page.

Don't lose time let's get started

Monday

Tuesday

Wednesday

Thursday

Friday

Saturday

Sunday

Monday

Tuesday

Wednesday

Thursday

Friday

Saturday

Sunday

Monday	
Tuesday	
Wednesday	
Thursday	
Friday	
Saturday	
Sunday	

Monday

Tuesday

Wednesday

Thursday

Friday

Saturday

Sunday

Monday	
Tuesday	
Wednesday	
Thursday	
Friday	
Saturday	
Sunday	

Monday

Tuesday

Wednesday

Thursday

Friday

Saturday

Sunday

Monday

Tuesday

Wednesday

Thursday

Friday

Saturday

Sunday

Monday

Tuesday

Wednesday

Thursday

Friday

Saturday

Sunday

Monday	
Tuesday	
Wednesday	
Thursday	
Friday	
Saturday	
Sunday	

Monday

Tuesday

Wednesday

Thursday

Friday

Saturday

Sunday

Monday	
Tuesday	
Wednesday	
Thursday	
Friday	
Saturday	
Sunday	

Monday

Tuesday

Wednesday

Thursday

Friday

Saturday

Sunday

Monday

Tuesday

Wednesday

Thursday

Friday

Saturday

Sunday

Monday

Tuesday

Wednesday

Thursday

Friday

Saturday

Sunday

Monday

Tuesday

Wednesday

Thursday

Friday

Saturday

Sunday

Monday

Tuesday

Wednesday

Thursday

Friday

Saturday

Sunday

Monday

Tuesday

Wednesday

Thursday

Friday

Saturday

Sunday

Monday

Tuesday

Wednesday

Thursday

Friday

Saturday

Sunday

Monday

Tuesday

Wednesday

Thursday

Friday

Saturday

Sunday

Monday	
Tuesday	
Wednesday	
Thursday	
Friday	
Saturday	
Sunday	

Monday

Tuesday

Wednesday

Thursday

Friday

Saturday

Sunday

Monday	
Tuesday	
Wednesday	
Thursday	
Friday	
Saturday	
Sunday	

Monday

Tuesday

Wednesday

Thursday

Friday

Saturday

Sunday

Monday	
Tuesday	
Wednesday	
Thursday	
Friday	
Saturday	
Sunday	

Monday

Tuesday

Wednesday

Thursday

Friday

Saturday

Sunday

Monday	
Tuesday	
Wednesday	
Thursday	
Friday	
Saturday	
Sunday	

Monday	
Tuesday	
Wednesday	
Thursday	
Friday	
Saturday	
Sunday	

Monday	
Tuesday	
Wednesday	
Thursday	
Friday	
Saturday	
Sunday	

Monday

Tuesday

Wednesday

Thursday

Friday

Saturday

Sunday

Monday

Tuesday

Wednesday

Thursday

Friday

Saturday

Sunday

Monday

Tuesday

Wednesday

Thursday

Friday

Saturday

Sunday

Monday	
Tuesday	
Wednesday	
Thursday	
Friday	
Saturday	
Sunday	

Monday

Tuesday

Wednesday

Thursday

Friday

Saturday

Sunday

Monday

Tuesday

Wednesday

Thursday

Friday

Saturday

Sunday

Monday

Tuesday

Wednesday

Thursday

Friday

Saturday

Sunday

Monday

Tuesday

Wednesday

Thursday

Friday

Saturday

Sunday

Monday	
Tuesday	
Wednesday	
Thursday	
Friday	
Saturday	
Sunday	

Monday	

Tuesday	

Wednesday	

Thursday	

Friday	

Saturday	

Sunday	

Monday

Tuesday

Wednesday

Thursday

Friday

Saturday

Sunday

Monday	
Tuesday	
Wednesday	
Thursday	
Friday	
Saturday	
Sunday	

Monday

Tuesday

Wednesday

Thursday

Friday

Saturday

Sunday

Monday

Tuesday

Wednesday

Thursday

Friday

Saturday

Sunday

Monday

Tuesday

Wednesday

Thursday

Friday

Saturday

Sunday

Monday

Tuesday

Wednesday

Thursday

Friday

Saturday

Sunday

Monday	
Tuesday	
Wednesday	
Thursday	
Friday	
Saturday	
Sunday	

Monday

Tuesday

Wednesday

Thursday

Friday

Saturday

Sunday

Monday	
Tuesday	
Wednesday	
Thursday	
Friday	
Saturday	
Sunday	

Monday

Tuesday

Wednesday

Thursday

Friday

Saturday

Sunday

Monday

Tuesday

Wednesday

Thursday

Friday

Saturday

Sunday

Monday	
Tuesday	
Wednesday	
Thursday	
Friday	
Saturday	
Sunday	

Monday	
Tuesday	
Wednesday	
Thursday	
Friday	
Saturday	
Sunday	

Monday

Tuesday

Wednesday

Thursday

Friday

Saturday

Sunday

Monday

Tuesday

Wednesday

Thursday

Friday

Saturday

Sunday

Monday	
Tuesday	
Wednesday	
Thursday	
Friday	
Saturday	
Sunday	

Monday

Tuesday

Wednesday

Thursday

Friday

Saturday

Sunday

Monday

Tuesday

Wednesday

Thursday

Friday

Saturday

Sunday

Monday

Tuesday

Wednesday

Thursday

Friday

Saturday

Sunday

Monday	
Tuesday	
Wednesday	
Thursday	
Friday	
Saturday	
Sunday	

Monday	
Tuesday	
Wednesday	
Thursday	
Friday	
Saturday	
Sunday	

Monday

Tuesday

Wednesday

Thursday

Friday

Saturday

Sunday

Monday

Tuesday

Wednesday

Thursday

Friday

Saturday

Sunday

Monday

Tuesday

Wednesday

Thursday

Friday

Saturday

Sunday

Monday

Tuesday

Wednesday

Thursday

Friday

Saturday

Sunday

Monday	
Tuesday	
Wednesday	
Thursday	
Friday	
Saturday	
Sunday	

Monday

Tuesday

Wednesday

Thursday

Friday

Saturday

Sunday

Monday	
Tuesday	
Wednesday	
Thursday	
Friday	
Saturday	
Sunday	

Monday

Tuesday

Wednesday

Thursday

Friday

Saturday

Sunday

Monday	
Tuesday	
Wednesday	
Thursday	
Friday	
Saturday	
Sunday	

Monday	
Tuesday	
Wednesday	
Thursday	
Friday	
Saturday	
Sunday	

Monday

Tuesday

Wednesday

Thursday

Friday

Saturday

Sunday

Monday

Tuesday

Wednesday

Thursday

Friday

Saturday

Sunday

Monday

Tuesday

Wednesday

Thursday

Friday

Saturday

Sunday

Monday

Tuesday

Wednesday

Thursday

Friday

Saturday

Sunday

Monday

Tuesday

Wednesday

Thursday

Friday

Saturday

Sunday

Monday	
Tuesday	
Wednesday	
Thursday	
Friday	
Saturday	
Sunday	

Monday	
Tuesday	
Wednesday	
Thursday	
Friday	
Saturday	
Sunday	

Monday

Tuesday

Wednesday

Thursday

Friday

Saturday

Sunday

Monday

Tuesday

Wednesday

Thursday

Friday

Saturday

Sunday

Monday

Tuesday

Wednesday

Thursday

Friday

Saturday

Sunday

Monday

Tuesday

Wednesday

Thursday

Friday

Saturday

Sunday

Monday

Tuesday

Wednesday

Thursday

Friday

Saturday

Sunday

Monday	
Tuesday	
Wednesday	
Thursday	
Friday	
Saturday	
Sunday	

Monday	
Tuesday	
Wednesday	
Thursday	
Friday	
Saturday	
Sunday	

Monday	
Tuesday	
Wednesday	
Thursday	
Friday	
Saturday	
Sunday	

Monday	
Tuesday	
Wednesday	
Thursday	
Friday	
Saturday	
Sunday	

Monday

_____
_____
_____

Tuesday

_____
_____
_____

Wednesday

_____
_____
_____

Thursday

_____
_____
_____

Friday

_____
_____
_____

Saturday

_____
_____
_____

Sunday

_____
_____
_____

Monday	
Tuesday	
Wednesday	
Thursday	
Friday	
Saturday	
Sunday	

Monday	
Tuesday	
Wednesday	
Thursday	
Friday	
Saturday	
Sunday	

Monday	
Tuesday	
Wednesday	
Thursday	
Friday	
Saturday	
Sunday	

Monday	
Tuesday	
Wednesday	
Thursday	
Friday	
Saturday	
Sunday	

Monday	
Tuesday	
Wednesday	
Thursday	
Friday	
Saturday	
Sunday	

Monday

Tuesday

Wednesday

Thursday

Friday

Saturday

Sunday

Monday

Tuesday

Wednesday

Thursday

Friday

Saturday

Sunday

Monday	
Tuesday	
Wednesday	
Thursday	
Friday	
Saturday	
Sunday	

Monday

Tuesday

Wednesday

Thursday

Friday

Saturday

Sunday

Monday

Tuesday

Wednesday

Thursday

Friday

Saturday

Sunday

Monday

Tuesday

Wednesday

Thursday

Friday

Saturday

Sunday

Monday

Tuesday

Wednesday

Thursday

Friday

Saturday

Sunday

Monday	
Monday	
Tuesday	
Wednesday	
Thursday	
Friday	
Saturday	
Sunday	

Monday	
Tuesday	
Wednesday	
Thursday	
Friday	
Saturday	
Sunday	

Monday	
Tuesday	
Wednesday	
Thursday	
Friday	
Saturday	
Sunday	

Monday

Tuesday

Wednesday

Thursday

Friday

Saturday

Sunday

Monday

Tuesday

Wednesday

Thursday

Friday

Saturday

Sunday

Monday	
Tuesday	
Wednesday	
Thursday	
Friday	
Saturday	
Sunday	

Monday	
Tuesday	
Wednesday	
Thursday	
Friday	
Saturday	
Sunday	

Monday

Tuesday

Wednesday

Thursday

Friday

Saturday

Sunday

Monday

Tuesday

Wednesday

Thursday

Friday

Saturday

Sunday

Printed in the USA
CPSIA information can be obtained
at www.ICGtesting.com
LVHW012252200923
758868LV00027B/742

9 798616 283023